Two Fridas

by F. Isabel Campoy
illustrated by Carol Heyer

Harcourt

Orlando   Boston   Dallas   Chicago   San Diego

Visit *The Learning Site!*

www.harcourtschool.com

My name is Frida. I was born in Mexico, but my family moved to California when I was three years old.

My mother, a painter herself, has always loved the paintings of Frida Kahlo. She decided to name me, her first daughter, after this great painter. She hoped I would be as smart and strong as the artist she admired.

Frida Kahlo was born in 1907 and died in
1954—not a very long life, but an interesting
one. She was married to Diego Rivera, the artist
famous for his murals of the Mexican people.
Frida and Diego were as different as two people
could be, but they loved each other dearly and
respected each other's work.

When I was very young, my mother let me use watercolors and finger paints. Later she bought me my own set of oil paints and paintbrushes. Of course my favorite class in school is art!

I like to paint scenes from around my neighborhood and send them to my grandparents in Mexico. They tell me they like my paintings better than photographs. They show my paintings to my aunts, uncles, and cousins in Mexico, too.

Last summer my grandparents came to California to visit. This summer we went to Mexico to visit them. My mother wanted to take me to the Casa Azul in Mexico City. The Casa Azul is now a museum, but it used to be the home of Frida Kahlo.

Casa Azul means "blue house." It really is a bright blue house. On the walls inside are many of Frida Kahlo's paintings. The museum also has some of the furniture that Frida Kahlo used!

It was so exciting to see these things that once belonged to Frida Kahlo! My mother told me she had waited until now to take me to Casa Azul because she wanted me to be old enough to remember what I saw there.

I spent a lot of time in each room of the museum. I wanted to remember everything. In the gift shop, I bought postcards that showed Frida Kahlo's paintings. I would put these postcards up in my room when I got home.

When school started this year, there were two new girls in my class. Carmela is from Argentina and Mu Lan is from China. There was also a new boy named Eric, who had moved here from Florida.

The students in my class welcomed Carmela and Mu Lan. At lunchtime, my friends and I invited them to sit with us. Mu Lan and Carmela didn't speak much English, but no one seemed to mind.

Suddenly I noticed that nobody was paying attention to the other new student, Eric. He looked lonely sitting by himself. I wondered if I should sit with him, but I thought my friends wouldn't like it if I did.

The only person who talked to Eric was our teacher, Mr. Caldwell. Eric had the right answers to Mr. Caldwell's questions. He seemed to be very smart.

The other students stared at Eric a lot. They didn't tease him, but they didn't say anything to him, either.

When I got home from school, I told my
mother about the new girls, Carmela and Mu
Lan. I mentioned that we had invited them to
eat with us.

I also told her about Eric. I said that no one
talked to him except Mr. Caldwell.

"Why do the students ignore him?" my
mother asked. I said I thought it was because
Eric was in a wheelchair.

"Why don't you talk to him, Frida?" my mother asked. I told her that I had wanted to sit with him at lunchtime but had held back. "I was afraid my friends would stop talking to me," I said.

My mother was surprised. She said she knew I was smart and strong, just like Frida Kahlo. "You should never be afraid to be kind to another person," she said. I knew she was right.

I wanted to learn more about Frida Kahlo. I went to the library and borrowed two books about her life. Once I started reading the first book, I couldn't put it down. What I read was so interesting!

My mother was right. Frida Kahlo was smart and strong. I felt proud to be named for someone so brave and talented.

Frida Kahlo did a lot of great things, but her life was very hard. Something terrible happened to her when she was young. It changed her life forever.

Frida Kahlo was in a very bad bus accident when she was eighteen. The doctors didn't think she would live. She had a lot of broken bones.

Frida Kahlo never fully healed from the accident. She learned to walk again, but she was in a lot of pain for the rest of her life.

I started thinking about Eric. I wondered why he was in a wheelchair. I also wondered if he had a lot of pain, as Frida Kahlo did. I decided I was going to talk to Eric and get to know him.

The next day in class I smiled at Eric. He seemed surprised, but he smiled back.

At lunchtime, I saw Eric sitting by himself again. Carmela and Mu Lan were sitting with their new friends and having a good time.

I told my friends that I was going to talk to Eric. I walked over to his table and asked if I could sit with him.

I introduced myself to Eric, and we talked about school. Then I asked him why he used a wheelchair. He told me that he had been in a car accident two years ago. He said he was unconscious for a long time. When he woke up, he couldn't feel or move his legs. He would never be able to walk again.

I told Eric that the woman I was named for had also been in an accident. I told him a little about Frida Kahlo's life and about what a great artist she was.

Eric told me that he played the violin. "Someday I want to be a famous violinist," he told me.

"Then you are an artist, too!" I said.

I was glad I had gotten to know Eric. I told
my friends that he played the violin, and they
all thought that was great. When they saw me
talking to Eric, they started talking to him, too.

I was happy that I had helped an artist make
friends. I felt sure that Frida Kahlo would be
pleased!

16